Thoracic and Cora

In Two Families

Columbidae and Hirundinidae

Marion Anne Jenkinson

Alpha Editions

This edition published in 2023

ISBN : 9789357947978

Design and Setting By
Alpha Editions
www.alphaedis.com
Email - info@alphaedis.com

As per information held with us this book is in Public Domain.
This book is a reproduction of an important historical work. Alpha Editions uses the
best technology to reproduce historical work in the same manner it was first
published to preserve its original nature. Any marks or number seen are left
intentionally to preserve its true form.

Contents

INTRODUCTION

Most descriptions of the circulatory system of birds, largely the work of Glenny, have dealt with arteries of the neck and thorax in a wide variety of species. As a result of his work, Glenny offered several hypotheses concerning the phylogenetic, hence taxonomic, significance of differences in some of these vessels. He also described six types of thoracic arterial arrangements and stated that these categories might represent various levels of evolution (Glenny, 1955:543-544).

The families Columbidae (pigeons) and Hirundinidae (swallows) have two nearly extreme arterial types described by Glenny, and are universally acknowledged as monophyletic. Differences within the families, therefore, can be considered as valid intrafamilial differences. I have investigated the thoracic and coracoid arteries and their branches in members of these two families to determine the degree of individual variability of the vessels, and the possible causes of interspecific and intrafamilial differences.

METHODS AND MATERIALS

All specimens studied are in The University of Kansas Museum of Natural History. They were preserved in alcohol and their blood vessels were not injected. Dissections were made with the aid of a binocular microscope at magnifications of 10× and 20×.

Following is a list of the species studied, the number of individuals of each species dissected, and the catalogue numbers of the specimens. The nomenclature and classification are those of the American Ornithologists' Union's *Check-List of North American Birds*, fifth edition (1957).

Family Columbidae

Zenaidura macroura (Linnaeus), Mourning Dove 2: 40325, 40326.*Zenaida asiatica* (Linnaeus), White-winged Dove 1: 40328.*Scardafella inca* (Lesson), Inca Dove 5: 34894, 34896, 34902, 34906, 34907.*Columba livia* Gmelin, Rock Dove (domestic pigeon) 1: 40321.

Family Hirundinidae

Iridoprocne bicolor (Vieillot), Tree Swallow 1: 38101.*Progne subis* (Linnaeus), Purple Martin 5: 37711, 38794, 38796, 38798, 38804.*Stelgidopteryx ruficollis* (Vieillot), Rough-winged Swallow 1: 38277.*Riparia riparia* (Linnaeus), Bank Swallow 2: 38784, 38785.*Hirundo rustica* (Linnaeus), Barn Swallow 1: 38839.

The following descriptions are of *Progne subis* and *Scardafella inca*. Differences in the vascular system in other members of the families represented by *P. subis* and *S. inca* are mentioned at the appropriate places. The muscles briefly described for each of these two species are those that are supplied by the thoracic or coracoid arteries or by branches of the same, and muscles that, by their origin, location, or insertion, seem to affect the course or origin of one of these arteries.

The following sources have been particularly useful for the terminology of muscles and of skeletal features: Ashley (1941), Beddard (1898), Coues (1903), Howard (1929), Howell (1937), and Hudson and Lanzillotti (1955).

The names used for most arteries are those in common usage for vertebrates. I have not used the terms "internal mammary" and "intercostal" artery as substitutes for "thoracic" artery, except when referring to the work of others. The vessel's homology with the internal mammary artery of mammals has been denied (Glenny, 1955:541), and the name "mammary" is certainly not useful descriptively in birds. The term "intercostal" is less objectionable, except that such a name may call to mind segmental vessels arising from the dorsal aorta. The term "thoracic" seems best, as it is reasonably descriptive, and has been used by Glenny in the majority of his descriptions covering a wide variety of birds. The name "sternoclavicular" has been used by others as a synonym for the "coracoid" artery. I have arbitrarily chosen to use the latter.

ACKNOWLEDGMENTS

I gratefully acknowledge many valuable suggestions in my research and the preparation of this manuscript from Professors Theodore H. Eaton, A. Byron Leonard, Richard F. Johnston, Robert M. Mengel, and E. Raymond Hall. Mr. Abbot S. Gaunt and Miss Sandra Lovett assisted in collecting specimens. Final drafts of the illustrations were prepared by Mr. Thomas Swearingen.

MYOLOGY AND ANGIOLOGY: HIRUNDINIDAE

Figs. 1, 2, 3, and 4 illustrate the following muscles and arteries described for *Progne subis*.

Myology

M. pectoralis thoracica, Fig. 1. The origin is from slightly less than the posterior half of the sternum, from the ventral half of the keel, almost the entire length of the posterolateral surface of the clavicle and adjacent portion of the sterno-coraco-clavicular membrane, and tendinously from the ventral thoracic ribs. This massive muscle covers the entire ventral surface of the thorax and converges to insert on the ventral side of the humerus on the pectoral surface.

M. supracoracoideus, Fig. 1. The origin is from the dorsal portion of the keel and medial portion of the sternum, and is bordered ventrally by the origin of M. pectoralis thoracica, and laterally by *M. coracobrachialis posterior*. The origin is also from the manubrium and the anterolateral portion of the proximal half of the coracoid and to a slight extent from the sterno-coraco-clavicular membrane adjacent to the manubrium. This large pinnate muscle converges, passes through the foramen triosseum, and inserts by a tendon on the external tuberosity of the humerus, immediately proximal to the insertion of *M. pectoralis thoracica*.

M. coracobrachialis posterior, Figs. 1 and 3. The origin is from the dorsolateral half of the coracoid, anterolateral portion of the sternum (where the area of origin is bordered medially by *M. supracoracoideus*, posteriorly by *M. pectoralis thoracica*, and laterally by *M. sternocoracoideus*), and also to a slight extent from the area of attachment of the thoracic ribs to the sternum. The muscle fibers converge along the lateral edge of the coracoid and insert on the median crest of the humerus immediately proximal to the pneumatic foramen. In passing from the origin on the sternum to the insertion on the humerus, the belly of the muscle bridges the angle formed by the costal process of the sternum and the coracoid.

M. sternocoracoideus, Figs. 2 and 3. The origin is from the entire external surface of the costal process of the sternum, and to a small extent from the extreme proximal ends of the thoracic ribs where they articulate with the costal process. The muscle inserts on a triangular area on the dorsomedial surface of the coracoid. Like *M. coracobrachialis posterior*, this muscle bridges the angle formed by the costal process and the coracoid.

M. subcoracoideus (ventral head), Figs. 2 and 3. The origin is from the dorsomedial edge of the coracoid at its extreme proximal end, and to a slight extent from the adjacent portion of the manubrium. The origin is medial to the insertion of *M. sternocoracoideus*. The ventral head passes anterodorsally along the medial edge of the coracoid and joins the dorsal head (not here described). The combined muscle then inserts by a tendon onto the internal tuberosity of the humerus.

M. costi-sternalis, Figs. 1, 2, and 3. The origin is from the anterior edge of the sternal portion of the first four thoracic ribs. This triangular muscle narrows and inserts on the posterior edge of the apex of the costal process. The portion arising from the first rib may share slips with *M. sternocoracoideus*.

M. costi-sternalis anterior, Figs. 1, 2, and 3. This muscle is variously developed, and originates from a small area on the ventral end of the vertebral portion of the last cervical rib. The insertion is on the apex of the costal process, immediately anterior to the insertion of *M. costi-sternalis*.

Mm. intercostales externus, Fig. 1. These muscles extend posteroventrally between the vertebral portions of successive thoracic ribs, and between the last cervical and first thoracic ribs. In the more posterior intercostal spaces these muscles are poorly developed, but they become progressively better developed anteriorly, and are fully represented in the most anterior intercostal spaces.

Mm. intercostales internus, Fig. 3. These muscles resemble the external intercostal muscles, but extend anteroventrally, with the muscles being most fully developed posteriorly, and progressively less so anteriorly.

Costopulmonary muscles, Fig. 3. This diagonal series of muscle slips from the thoracic ribs attaches to the aponeurosis covering the lungs.

Angiology

Figs. 3 and 4 show all arteries discussed for this family. The numbers following the names or descriptions of arteries in the text refer to numbered arteries in one or both of these figures.

The right and left innominate or brachiocephalic arteries arise from the aortic trunk and give rise to the common carotid arteries (14). The major vessel continuing across the thoracic cavity is the subclavian artery. Classically the subclavian is considered as continuing into the anterior appendage as the axillary artery. However, in the species studied, the axillary artery can best be described as a branch from the subclavian; the pectoral stem forms a more direct continuation of the subclavian. In traversing the thoracic cavity, the subclavian gives rise to the thoracic, coracoid, and axillary arteries, and leaves the thoracic cavity as the pectoral trunk, dorsal to the area where *Mm. coracobrachialis posterior* and *sternocoracoideus* span the angle formed by the coracoid and costal process.

The pectoral trunk bifurcates into two main pectoral arteries (9), which penetrate *M. pectoralis thoracica*. Neither the axillary artery nor these pectoral arteries were traced in my study.

The coracoid artery (2) arises from the ventral face of the subclavian (1), either opposite the base of, or medial to, the axillary artery (10). The coracoid artery passes ventrad between the medial edge of the coracoid and the ventral head of *M. subcoracoideus*, and an artery (7) is given off to supply that muscle. The main vessel then penetrates *M. supracoracoideus* and bifurcates or ramifies into several vessels (12).

Between the origin of the coracoid artery from the subclavian, and the point where the coracoid artery passes the medial edge of the coracoid, several branches are given off. These vessels are highly variable in origin, as described below, and not all were always found. Along with the coracoid artery, they are termed a "coracoid complex."

The first artery (11) of this complex arises from any one of several places: from the lateral face of the coracoid artery at its base; independently from the subclavian immediately lateral to the origin of the coracoid artery; and from the thoracic artery near its origin. This vessel travels laterad, parallel to the subclavian, and penetrates *M. coracobrachialis posterior* at the same point that the pectoral artery passes dorsal to that muscle.

Another vessel (common stem of 4 and 5) of the coracoid complex in most specimens arises from the anterior face of the coracoid artery and branches into several vessels, some of which (5) supply *M. subcoracoideus*, and some of which (4) feed *M. coracobrachialis posterior*. The vessel occasionally shares a common stem with the main vessel (11) to *M. coracobrachialis posterior*, and in some specimens arises independently from the subclavian, immediately anterior to the origin of the coracoid artery. The branch (4) to *M. coracobrachialis posterior* was also seen to arise independently from any of the above-mentioned positions.

Two remaining vessels (6 and 8) are often found as branches from the coracoid artery. They were small and often were collapsed in the individuals I dissected, but were most clearly seen in *Iridoprocne bicolor*. The vessels occasionally had a common base, and in some specimens only one vessel was found. The first artery (6) passes mediad into *M. sternocoracoideus*, or continues across that muscle onto the inner face of the sternum. The second vessel (8) also supplies *M. sternocoracoideus* or the inner surface of the sternum, and often a large branch continues across the dorsal surface of the coracoid to *M. coracobrachialis posterior*. Fig. 3 shows a composite of these vessels; not all branches were seen in any one specimen. In the specimen of *I. bicolor* a foramen existed on the lateral edge of the coracoid where the branch (of 8) to *M. coracobrachialis posterior* passed. An examination of skeletons of five to

10 individuals each of the five species for which dissections were made, and of *Petrochelidon pyrrhonota* (Cliff Swallow) and *Tachycineta thalassina* (Violet-green Swallow), in the University of Kansas collection, showed that most coracoids of these seven species of swallows had a small notch (as shown in Fig. 4) or a complete foramen there.

The thoracic artery (3) arises from the subclavian opposite the base of the coracoid artery, or from the base of the coracoid artery. Of the five specimens of *P. subis* dissected, one individual had the former arrangement on both sides, and one had the latter on both sides, whereas in the remaining three the thoracic artery arose from the coracoid artery on one side and from the subclavian on the other side. The distance between these two possible sites of origin is slight.

The thoracic artery usually passes ventral to *M. costi-sternalis anterior*. Occasionally a small artery (13) could be traced from the main trunk of the thoracic artery to that muscle. The main thoracic artery bifurcates near the insertion of *M. costi-sternalis*, the branches traveling posteriad on both sides of the muscle. On one side of one specimen this artery bifurcated immediately after leaving the subclavian, the dorsal trunk passing dorsal to *M. costi-sternalis anterior*, and the ventral trunk ventral to the muscle. On the other side of the same individual the artery passed dorsal to *M. costi-sternalis anterior*, bifurcating at the normal point.

From the ventral trunk of the thoracic artery a variable number of small vessels arises to supply the costosternal articulations. The main ventral trunk bifurcates into two branches, one of which passes onto the inner face of the sternum, and one of which supplies the posterior two intercostal spaces.

The dorsal thoracic trunk supplies *M. costi-sternalis*, several dorsal intercostal areas, and the costopulmonary muscles. Minor variations in all of the smaller branches of the thoracic artery were common.

MYOLOGY AND ANGIOLOGY: COLUMBIDAE

Figs. 5, 6, and 7 illustrate the following muscles and arteries described for *Scardafella inca*.

Myology

M. pectoralis thoracica, Fig. 5. The origin is from approximately the ventral third of the keel, the lateral and anterior portion of the clavicle and the adjacent sterno-coraco-clavicular membrane, and from the lateral portion of the sternum and the fascia overlying the thoracic ribs. This massive muscle covers the entire ventral surface of the thorax, converges, and inserts on the pectoral surface on the ventral side of the humerus.

M. supracoracoideus, Fig. 5. The origin is from the dorsal two-thirds of the keel and medial half of the sternum (where the origin is bordered ventrally, posteriorly, and laterally by the origin of *M. pectoralis thoracica*) and from the sterno-coraco-clavicular membrane adjacent to the coracoid. This large pinnate muscle converges, passes through the foramen triosseum, and inserts by means of a strong tendon on the dorsal surface of the humerus on the deltoid ridge.

M. coracobrachialis posterior, Fig. 5. The origin is from a prominent lateral wing on the posterolateral portion of the coracoid, and from the lateral surface of the proximal two-thirds of the coracoid. The insertion is by means of a tendon on the internal tuberosity of the humerus. Of the muscles described here, this one differs most strikingly from the homologous muscle in *P. subis*. The difference can be seen by comparing Figs. 1 and 5.

M. sternocoracoideus, Figs. 5, 6, and 7. The origin is from the external, and to a slight extent from the internal, surface of the costal process. The insertion is on a posterolateral triangular area on the dorsal surface of the coracoid.

M. costi-sternalis, Figs. 5 and 6. The origin is from the anterior edge of the sternal portion of the first three thoracic ribs. The muscle converges and inserts on the apex of the costal process.

M. subcoracoideus (ventral head), Fig. 6. The origin is from the manubrium and from approximately the posterior half of the coracoid and on the medial and dorsal surface of that bone, and the medial side of the sterno-coraco-clavicular membrane adjacent to the coracoid. The ventral head passes anterodorsally to join with the dorsal head (not here described), and the combined muscle inserts by a tendon on the internal tuberosity of the humerus.

Mm. intercostales externus, Fig. 5. These muscles extend posteroventrally between successive thoracic ribs and between the last cervical and first thoracic ribs.

Mm. intercostales internus, Fig. 7. These muscles extend anteroventrally between the last three thoracic ribs.

Costopulmonary muscles, Fig. 7. This series of muscle slips from the thoracic ribs attaches to the aponeurosis covering the lungs.

Angiology

Figs. 5, 6, and 7 show all arteries discussed for this family. The numbers following names or descriptions of arteries in the text refer to numbered arteries in one of these figures. Insofar as possible, the numbers used for these arteries are the same numbers used for the homologous vessels in swallows.

The right and left innominate arteries arise from the aortic trunk and give rise to the common carotid (14) and subclavian (1) arteries. The latter continues across the thoracic cavity, giving rise to the coracoid (2) and axillary (10) arteries, and becoming the pectoral trunk. That trunk swings posteriorly and leaves the thoracic cavity near the apex of the costal process, as shown in Fig. 7. Where the trunk passes under *M. sternocoracoideus*, the thoracic artery (3) is given off.

The various branches of the coracoid artery, again referred to as a "coracoid complex," are as follows: The first branch, from the posterior face of the coracoid artery, is a relatively large vessel (6) here termed the sternal artery; it passes mediad across *M. sternocoracoideus*, sending off a branch (6a) to that muscle. The right sternal artery continues posteriorly on the mid-line of the inner surface of the sternum, and appears to send branches into the various pneumatic foramina of the sternum, but these vessels are minute and exceedingly difficult to trace accurately. The corresponding left vessel is smaller and ramifies on the anteromedial surface of the sternum. Variations found in these vessels were the following: In one specimen of *S. inca* the sternal artery had, on both sides, an independent origin from the subclavian, lateral to the origin of the coracoid artery. In *Zenaidura macroura* both right and left sternal arteries were similar to the left vessel described above, no median longitudinal vessel being seen. In *Columba livia* no vessel corresponding to the sternal artery was seen. In *Zenaida asiatica* these arteries penetrated *M. sternocoracoideus*; no branch to the sternum was seen.

A small complex of vessels (4 and 4a) arises from the lateral face of the coracoid artery and feeds *M. coracobrachialis posterior*, and occasionally *M. sternocoracoideus*. One branch (4a) passes under the coracoid and travels along the lateral side of that bone, supplying small branches to *M. coracobrachialis posterior*, and finally ramifying on the head of the coracoid. In *C. livia*, *Zenaidura macroura*, and *Zenaida asiatica* this complex usually arises independently from the subclavian, and in one case it arose from the axillary artery.

Two other branches from the coracoid artery were regularly seen. The first (8) passes across *M. sternocoracoideus* and appears to supply the area of the coracoid articulation with the sternum; the second (7) supplies *M. subcoracoideus* as the main vessel passes between that muscle and the coracoid and penetrates *M. suparacoracoideus*. A small notch on the medial side of the coracoid (shown in Figs. 6 and 7) often marks the passage of the coracoid artery.

All vessels of the coracoid complex are exceedingly variable, in number, size, and site of origin.

A prominent vessel (15) is given off from the posterior pectoral artery, outside the thoracic cavity, passes ventrad, and sends two branches into *M. supracoracoideus*. No corresponding artery was seen in the swallows dissected.

The thoracic artery (3), arising from the pectoral stem, characteristically bifurcates at the anterior end of *M. costi-sternalis*. The dorsal, and larger, branch passes posteriorly, sends several small branches to *M. costi-sternalis*, and continues to the most posterior rib. The ventral trunk bifurcates, one branch passing along the edge of, and supplying, *M. costi-sternalis*, the other branch passing onto the surface of the sternum. In some specimens two such branches to the sternum were seen.

SUMMARY OF ARTERIAL ARRANGEMENT

In both families the vessels that are relatively constant in appearance are: a subclavian giving rise to the carotid and axillary arteries, and becoming the pectoral trunk; the thoracic artery arising variously, and passing posteriorly to the rib cage; and the coracoid complex of vessels. The coracoid complex includes the coracoid artery, the vessels to *Mm. sternocoracoideus* and *coracobrachialis posterior*, and the sternal artery, which is variously present, and more extensive in some species than in others.

DISCUSSION AND CONCLUSIONS

In the vessels studied individual variation is marked, but the arterial arrangement within both families is relatively constant. Interfamilial differences probably represent responses of the arteries to adaptive structural differences of other systems of the body.

Individual Variation

The term "individual variation" is used here to mean "continuous non-sex-associated variation" (see Mayr, Linsley, and Usinger, 1953:93) found between members of the same species or between the two sides of the same individual. It is hazardous to define individual variation (and also interspecific differences, as discussed later) in the origin of one vessel by relating its location to other vessels, because these may likewise vary in origin. But, by necessity, certain vessels that are probably less variable (axillary, carotid, and pectoral arteries) have been considered here as being constant in origin. If these three vessels are accepted as reference points, individual variants, as well as interspecific differences, can easily be described in the thoracic and coracoid arteries and in their various branches.

The thoracic artery in *P. subis* arose either from the subclavian artery, or from the coracoid artery. Likewise in other swallows, both of these origins were found. In doves the thoracic artery arose consistently from the pectoral stem, lateral to the origin of the axillary artery.

The coracoid artery in *P. subis* and other swallows arose from the subclavian artery, either opposite the base of the axillary artery, or medial to that vessel. In all doves studied the coracoid artery arose from the subclavian medial to the axillary artery. I observed much individual variation in the branches of the coracoid artery (that is to say, in the vessels of the coracoid complex). In *S. inca* the sternal artery arose either from the coracoid artery, or independently from the subclavian. As mentioned earlier, in members of both families the vessels to *Mm. coracobrachialis posterior* and *subcoracoideus* are highly variable, arising in swallows from the coracoid artery or from the subclavian artery, and in doves from either of these two sites or from the axillary artery. The distribution of these arteries after their origin is also diverse.

Individual variation in the arteries of the thorax has been recorded previously. Bhaduri, Biswas, and Das (1957:2) state that, in the domestic pigeon, "the origin and course of various smaller arteries... show noticeable variation," although they do not specifically state to which vessels they are referring. Fisher (1955:287-288) found variability in the Whooping Crane, *Grus americana*, of the axillary, coracoid, thoracic, and pectoral arteries. In one specimen he found these vessels arising on the right side from the subclavian, in the sequence just listed, and on the left side all arose from the same point. Berger (1956:439-440) strongly emphasized the variability of the vascular system, calling it the most variable in the body. As he stated, this high degree of individual variation seems to be due to the embryological development of the system, wherein many of the adult channels of circulation are derived from embryonic plexuses.

Intrafamilial Differences

In spite of the rather extensive amount of individual variability in some vessels, I found the over-all pattern of arteries to be relatively constant within the family Columbidae and within the family Hirundinidae. There are, nevertheless, several intrafamilial differences needing some further discussion and clarification.

Others have reported the occasional presence of more than one coracoid artery on each side in some columbids, these arteries being described as arising from various sites and being variously named. Bhaduri and Biswas (1954) described the arterial situation in seven species of the family Columbidae (*Columba livia, Streptopelia tranquebarica, S. chinensis, S. senegalensis, Chalcophaps indica, Treron bicincta,* and *T. phoenicoptera*) and stated (*op. cit.*: 348) that "The sternoclavicular [= coracoid] artery is similar in all the species, but the domestic pigeon seems to be unique in that it has, in addition, a small vessel, the accessory sternoclavicular." This artery was described later, in the domestic pigeon, as follows (Bhaduri, Biswas, and Das, 1957:5): "A minute and insignificant vessel which has been termed the *accessory sternoclavicular* artery... is given off close to the origin of the sternoclavicular. It passes anteroventrally to supply the adjacent muscles." Glenny (1955:577) described the arterial pattern characteristic of members of the family Columbidae (more than 30 species studied by him) and stated that "three pairs of coracoid arteries are found in *Otidiphaps nobilis*, normally one or two pairs may be found." As suggested by Bhaduri and Biswas (1954:348), the "accessory" vessel probably corresponds to a vessel previously described by Glenny (1940) in *Streptopelia chinensis* and referred to as the "coracoid minor."

Bhaduri and Biswas (1954:348) have suggested that "the accessory sternoclavicular artery occurring sporadically as it does in some species of diverse groups may not have any phylogenetic value."

In no case did I find more than one coracoid artery on a side. When one of the highly variable arteries feeding *Mm. coracobrachialis posterior* and *sternocoracoideus* (arteries 4 and 4a, Fig. 7) arises from the subclavian or axillary artery instead of from the coracoid artery, that vessel may have been interpreted by others as a second (accessory or minor) coracoid artery. If so, this artery probably does not "occur sporadically." Rather, its origin from the subclavian, axillary, or thoracic artery may be sporadic, subject to individual variation, and it may have been overlooked when it arose from the coracoid artery.

Of the vessels described here, the only one that differed distinctly in one species was the sternal artery. In *Scardafella inca* the right sternal vessel was long, extending down the mid-line of the inner surface of the sternum, whereas in other columbids the right and left arteries ramified on the anterior part of the inner surface of the sternum, or were altogether lacking. I am unable to account for the differential development of this artery in *S. inca*.

In describing the arterial arrangement in the seven species of Indian columbids named earlier, Bhaduri and Biswas (1954:348) state that all species except *Treron phoenicoptera* have two "internal mammary" arteries on each side "showing variable sites of origin." These arteries were later described (Bhaduri, Biswas, and Das, 1957:4-5) as "a slender (*outer*) *internal mammary* artery... to the outer wall of the thoracic cavity" and "a slender (*inner*) *internal mammary* artery... to supply the inner wall of the chest cavity." From this description, the question arises as to whether the "outer" one of these arteries should properly be called an *external* instead of *internal* mammary artery. In any case, I saw no specimen possessing two thoracic arteries on a side.

Interfamilial Differences

As shown above, there is a high degree of individual variation in the vessels being considered, while at the same time, few interspecific differences were noted within the families. On the other hand, the vascular arrangement of swallows consistently differed from that of pigeons in the species studied. The differences are most easily described by discussing the resulting change in the site of origin of the thoracic artery. In swallows the thoracic artery arises between the carotid and axillary arteries, either from the stem of the coracoid artery or independently from the subclavian, but in pigeons the thoracic artery arises from the pectoral stem, a site of attachment that is relatively more lateral than in swallows.

This difference, in my opinion, demonstrates well the topological relationships of various systems of the body, here especially of the skeletal, muscular, and vascular systems. The location of the thoracic artery seems to be determined by the particular configuration of skeletal and muscular elements, although even within the bounds set by these elements, individual variation in the precise origin of the artery is possible. In all swallows dissected *Mm. coracobrachialis posterior* and *sternocoracoideus* bridge the angle formed by the costal process and the coracoid. This arrangement makes it necessary for the subclavian to leave the thoracic cavity dorsal to the costal process, although it does pass immediately anterior to that process. The thoracic artery arises from the vessel next to the apex of the costal process, hence from the subclavian, between the axillary and carotid arteries.

In pigeons, the wing of the coracoid extends farther laterally than does the costal process, and the apex of the latter is displaced farther posteriorly than it is in swallows. *M. coracobrachialis posterior* does not arise from the sternum, and only part of the costal process serves as a point of origin for *M. sternocoracoideus*. Consequently, this region differs from that of swallows; the area between the costal process and coracoid is not entirely bridged by muscle, and the space between the two skeletal elements is of a different shape and size. It seems that these differences have resulted, in pigeons, in the subclavian assuming a more anterior position with reference to the costal process. The subclavian in these birds leads into the pectoral artery, which runs posteriad, passing under *M. sternocoracoideus* and leaving the thoracic cavity approximately opposite the apex of the costal process. The thoracic artery arises immediately opposite the apex of the costal process from the main artery in the area, as it does in swallows, except that in this case the adjacent artery from which it arises is the pectoral stem.

The thoracic area seems to be most "efficiently" arranged when the thoracic artery arises *opposite the apex of the costal process, from whatever main artery is closest to that site*. This arrangement existed in all species studied. Considering the differences in skeletal and muscular structures, between pigeons and swallows, it would be much more remarkable if an alternative were the case, that is to say if the thoracic artery *had the same site of attachment on the subclavian* in both groups.

A comparison of these suggestions with statements made previously about these arteries seems necessary. When Glenny (1955) summarized his accumulative findings, concerning the main arteries in the region of the heart, based on individuals representing more than 750 avian species of 27 orders and 120 families, he described five types of thoracic arteries that were distinguished by differences in the site of their origin, and one type in which there were two thoracic arteries on each side. His statements regarding these differences were as follows (Glenny, 1955:543-544):

"The thoracic, intercostal, or internal mammary artery of birds... is found to arise at slightly different relative positions—from a point at the base of the inferior pectoral artery to a point near the base of the coracoid or sternoclavicular artery, and in some instances both of these vessels have a common root from the subclavian artery. Such differences are found to be of common occurrence within several orders of birds. In the Galliformes and the Passeriformes there appears to be a graded series in the sites of attachment of the thoracic artery from a lateral to a medial position. As a result of these observations, numerical values can be assigned to the site of attachment of the intercostal or thoracic artery, and these values may come to be used as an index in specific levels of evolution....

"The medial migration of the thoracic artery appears to have some phylogenetic significance as yet not understood."

The six types of thoracic arteries described in Glenny's classification were distinguished as follows (Glenny, 1955:544):

"Type 1: attachment to the pectoral stem lateral to the axillary.

"Type 2: attachment to the subclavian between the axillary and coracoid.

"Type 3: attachment to the subclavian at the base of the coracoid.

"Type 4: attachment to the subclavian, but with a common root for both the coracoid and thoracic.

"Type 5: attachment to the subclavian medial to both the axillary and coracoid.

"Type 6: two separate thoracic arteries are present; the primary thoracic is the same as type 1 above, while the secondary thoracic is the same as type 3 or type 4 above."

Possibly the thoracic artery has undergone migration but apparent differences in its origin might well be due to differences in other vessels of the thoracic area. Additionally, there seems to be no reason to assume that the lateral position of the thoracic artery is the primitive one, or that the medial is the derived position, as is implied by the phrase "medial migration." Although the lateral site of attachment (type 1) is predominant in the lower orders of birds, and the medial attachment is found primarily in Passeriformes, a fact which may indicate that type 1 is the more primitive, it must nevertheless be kept in mind that a sequence of a single morphological character does not necessarily represent the phylogenetic sequence of the character itself (see Mayr, 1955:41).

Also, a given arterial arrangement might be independently derived more than once. If such has been the case, similarities in arterial arrangements in different taxa would sometimes be "chance similarities," that is to say, "resemblance in characteristics developed in separate taxa by independent causes and without causal relationship involving the similarity as such" (Simpson, 1961:79).

The particular arrangement of the arteries of the thoracic area also seems to be of limited value as a clue to taxonomic relationships. If the origin of any artery is determined by skeletal and muscular features, as I suggest, the artery perhaps ought not be considered as a separate character, but as part of a "character complex" that varies as a unit (see Mayr, Linsley, and Usinger,

1953:123). The skeleton offers a potential fossil record for consideration. Changes in the skeleton and muscles, great enough to affect the blood vessels, would probably be detected more easily than would the resulting vascular changes. Also, I did not find as much individual variation in the skeleton and muscles in the area studied as I did in the vascular system. In other words, within the bounds established by the skeletal and muscular features, the artery still exhibited individual variation in exact origin.

SUMMARY

The origin, distribution, and individual variation of the thoracic and coracoid arteries, and their branches, have been studied in four species of the family Columbidae (pigeons) and in five species of the family Hirundinidae (swallows). These arteries are described for *Scardafella inca* (Inca Dove) and *Progne subis* (Purple Martin). Muscles that are supplied by these vessels, and muscles the particular configuration of which seems to effect the arrangement of the arteries have also been described. Correlation of the arteries observed with those named and described by other workers has been attempted.

In most of the vessels studied there is a high degree of individual variation, but few interspecific differences were noticed within either family. Differences in the arteries of the thorax between the two families are described by discussing the resulting different origins of the thoracic artery. In swallows the thoracic artery arises from either the subclavian artery or the coracoid artery, whereas in pigeons it arises from the pectoral trunk. This difference in site of attachment seems to be a result of differences between the two families in muscular and skeletal elements of the thorax.

The particular site of attachment of the thoracic artery is of limited value as a taxonomic character. Several considerations influenced this conclusion. (1) If the location of the artery is determined by skeletal and muscular elements, these associated structures must be considered taxonomically as a "character complex" (a set of characters varying as a unit). (2) Even within the bounds established by the skeleton and muscles, the artery displays a high degree of individual variation in exact origin. (3) A given arterial arrangement could have been derived independently many times. (4) Because differences are defined relative to other likewise variable vessels, supposed similarities or differences in the one artery may be artifacts of the system of description.

My findings and interpretations do not support previous suggestions that the thoracic artery has undergone a mediad migration, and that the various sites of attachment of that vessel may come to represent various levels of evolution. The primitive site of attachment of the vessel is unknown, and it seems to me that it has not been sufficiently demonstrated that the vessel has undergone any "migration."

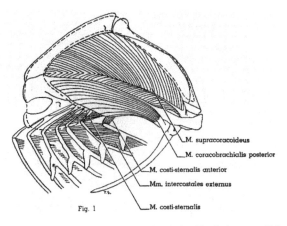

M. supracoracoideus
M. coracobrachialis posterior
M. costi-sternalis anterior
Mm. intercostales externus
Fig. 1
M. costi-sternalis

Fig. 1. *Progne subis.* Lateral view of left half of thorax. M. pectoralis thoracica (area of insertion indicated by dotted line) has been removed. Muscles not described in text are not shown. (× 1.5.)

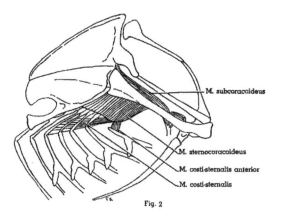

M. subcoracoideus
M. sternocoracoideus
M. costi-sternalis anterior
M. costi-sternalis
Fig. 2

Fig. 2. *Progne subis.* Lateral view of left half of thorax. Same view as shown in Fig. 1, but with Mm. supracoracoideus, coracobrachialis posterior, and intercostales externus removed. (× 1.5.)

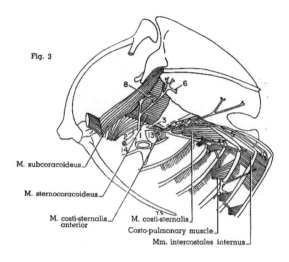

Fig. 3

M. subcoracoideus

M. sternocoracoideus

M. costi-sternalis anterior

M. costi-sternalis

Costo-pulmonary muscle

Mm. intercostales internus

Fig. 3. Progne subis. Medial view of left half of thorax. Not all muscles shown. See Fig. 4 for identification of arteries. (× 1.5.)

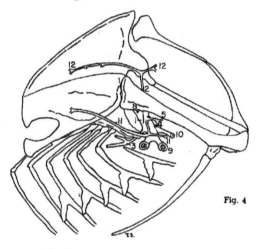

Fig. 4

Fig. 4. Progne subis. Lateral view of left half of thorax. (× 1.5.)

(Applies also to Fig. 3.)

1. Subclavian artery.2. Coracoid artery.3. Thoracic artery.4. (Unnamed.) Supplies *M. coracobrachialis posterior*.5. (Unnamed.) Supplies *M. subcoracoideus*.6. (Unnamed.) Supplies *M. sternocoracoideus* and sternum.7. (Unnamed.) Supplies *M. subcoracoideus*.8. (Unnamed.) Supplies *M. sternocoracoideus*, *M. coracobrachialis posterior*, and sternum.9. Pectoral artery.10. Axilliary artery.11. (Unnamed.) Supplies *M. coracobrachialis posterior*.12.

(Unnamed.) Supplies *M. supracoracoideus.*13. (Unnamed.) Supplies *M. costi-sternalis anterior.*14. Carotid artery.

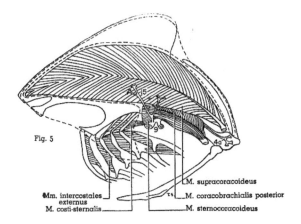

Fig. 5. Scardafella inca. Lateral view of left half of thorax. M. pectoralis thoracica (area of insertion indicated by dotted line) has been removed. Muscles not described in text are not shown. See legend for Fig. 7 for identification of arteries. (× 1.)

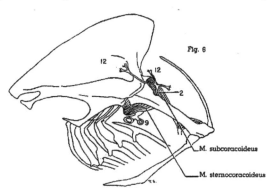

Fig. 6. Scardafella inca. Lateral view of left half of thorax. See legend for Fig. 7 for identification of arteries. (× 1.)

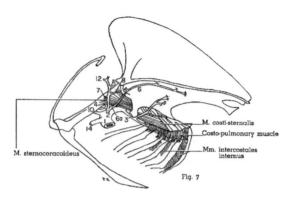

Fig. 7. Scardafella inca. Medial view of left half of thorax. (× 1.)

KEY

(Applies also to Figs. 5 and 6.) Numerals not used are those used for *Progne subis* for which no homologous artery occurs in *Scardafella inca.*

1. Subclavian artery.2. Coracoid artery.3. Thoracic artery.4. (Unnamed.) Supplies *Mm. coracobrachialis posterior* and *sternocoracoideus.*4a. (Unnamed.) Supplies *M. coracobrachialis posterior.*6. Sternal artery. (Shown as it appears on *right* side. Left sternal artery not so extensive.)6a. (Unnamed.) Supplies *M. sternocoracoideus.*7. (Unnamed.) Supplies *M. subcoracoideus.*8. (Unnamed.) Supplies coracoid-sternal articulation.9. Pectoral artery.10. Axillary artery.12. (Unnamed.) Supplies *M. supracoracoideus.*14. Carotid artery.15. (Unnamed.) Supplies *M. supracoracoideus.*

Milton Keynes UK
Ingram Content Group UK Ltd.
UKHW040121170324
439511UK00004B/162